Christmas Songs *for* Easy Piano

WISE PUBLICATIONS
London/New York/Paris/Sydney/Copenhagen/Madrid

Exclusive Distributors:

Music Sales Limited
8/9 Frith Street,
London W1V 5TZ, England.

Music Sales Pty Limited
120 Rothschild Avenue,
Rosebery, NSW 2018,
Australia.

Order No. AM951126
ISBN 0-7119-7240-0
This book © Copyright 1998 by Wise Publications

Compiled by Peter Evans
Music arranged by Stephen Duro
Music processed by Allegro Reproductions
Cover design by Chloë Alexander
Cover photograph courtesy of Telegraph Colour Library
Printed in the United Kingdom by Caligraving Limited,
Thetford, Norfolk.

Your Guarantee of Quality
As publishers, we strive to produce every book to the highest commercial
standards. The music has been freshly engraved and the book has been
carefully designed to minimise awkward page turns and to make playing
from it a real pleasure.
Particular care has been given to specifying acid-free, neutral-sized
paper made from pulps which have not been elemental chlorine
bleached. This pulp is from farmed sustainable forests and was produced
with special regard for the environment.
Throughout, the printing and binding have been planned to ensure a
sturdy, attractive publication which should give years of enjoyment.
If your copy fails to meet our high standards, please inform us and we
will gladly replace it.

Music Sales' complete catalogue describes thousands of titles and is
available in full colour sections by subject, direct from Music Sales
Limited. Please state your areas of interest and send a cheque/postal
order for £1.50 for postage to: Music Sales Limited, Newmarket Road,
Bury St. Edmunds, Suffolk IP33 3YB.

Visit the Internet Music Shop at
http://www.musicsales.co.uk

Contents

Christmas Alphabet

Words & Music by Buddy Kaye & Jules Loman

Moderately

"C" is for the Can-dy trimmed a-round the Christ-mas tree,

"H" is for the Hap-pi-ness with all the fa-mi-ly.

"R" is for the Rein-deer pran-cing by the win-dow pane. "I" is for the Ic-ing on the

cake as sweet as su-gar cane. "S" is for the Stock-ing

Good King Wenceslas

Traditional Christmas Carol

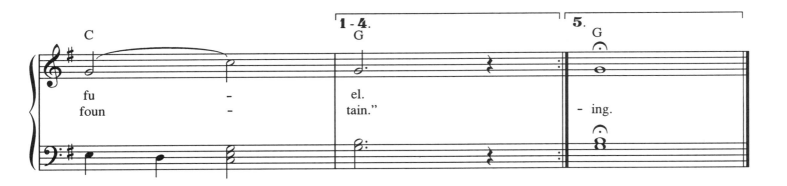

Verse 3:

"Bring me flesh and bring me wine,
Bring me pine logs hither;
Thou and I will see him dine,
When we bear them thither."
Page and monarch forth they went,
Onward both together,
Through the rude wind's wild lament,
And the bitter weather.

Verse 4:

"Sire, the night is darker now
And the wind blows stronger;
Fails my heart, I know not how,
I can go no longer."
"Mark my footsteps, good my page!
Tread thou in them boldly;
Thou shall find the winter's rage
Freeze thy blood less coldly."

Verse 5:

In his master's steps he trod,
Where the snow lay dinted;
Heat was in the very sod
Which the saint had printed.
Therefore, Christian men, be sure
Wealth or rank possessing
Ye, who now will bless the poor,
Shall yourselves find blessing.

Hark! The Herald Angels Sing

Christmas Carol

Verse 3:

Hail, the heaven born Prince of Peace!
Hail, the Son of righteousness!
Light and life to all He brings,
Risen with healing on His wings,
Mild He lays His glory by;
Born that man no more may die;
Born to raise the sons of earth;
Born to give them second birth.
    Hark! the herald angels sing,
    Glory to the new-born King!

I Believe In Father Christmas

Words by Peter Sinfield ♚ Music by Greg Lake

Christ - mas tree smell, and their eyes full of tin - sel and fire.
first light of dawn, And I saw him and through his dis - guise.

Verse 3:

I wish you a hopeful Christmas
I wish you a brave New Year;
All anguish, pain and sadness
Leave your heart and let your road be clear.
They said there'd be snow at Christmas,
They said there'd be peace on earth.
Hallelujah Noel be it heaven or hell,
The Christmas we get we deserve.

Jingle Bells

Traditional

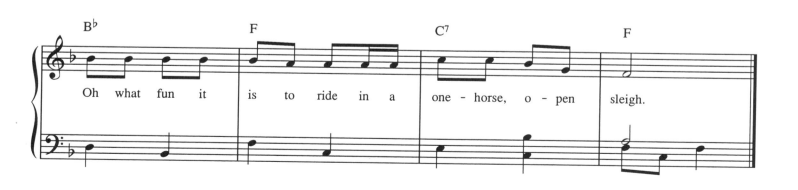

13

Last Christmas

Words & Music by George Michael

This year to save me from tears— I'll give it to some-one spe-cial.—

Once bit-ten and twice shy——— I keep my dis-tance but you still catch my eye.

Tell me ba-by, do you re-cog-nise me? Well, it's been a year, it does-n't sur-prise me.

To Coda ⊕

15

Happy Xmas (War Is Over)

Words & Music by John Lennon & Yoko Ono

3. And so this is Xmas for weak and for strong
   The rich and the poor ones the road is so long.
   And so, happy Xmas for black and for white
   For the yellow and red ones, let's stop all fights.
   A merry, merry Xmas and a happy New Year
   Let's hope it's a good one without any fear.

Mary's Boy Child

Words & Music by Jester Hairston

Fairly slow

3rd time to Coda

22

D.S. al Coda

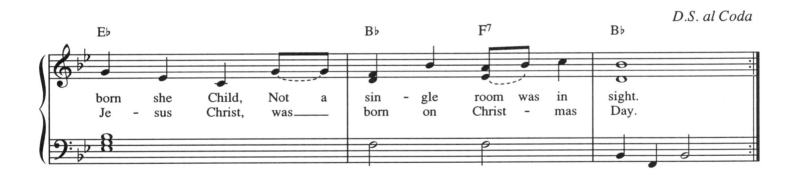

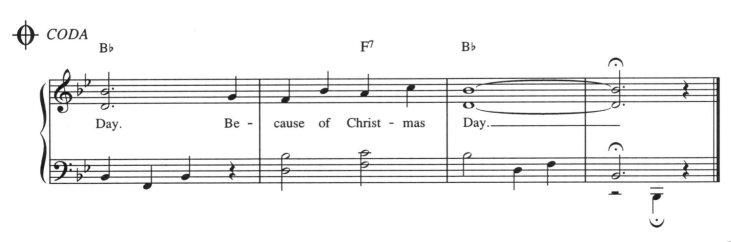

Merry Xmas Everybody

Words & Music by Neville Holder & James Lea

Verse 3:

Are you hanging up a stocking on your wall?
Are you hoping that the snow will start to fall?
Do you ride on down the hillside in a buggy you have made?
When you land upon your head then you 'bin slayed;

Mistletoe And Wine

Music by Keith Strachan ✤ Words by Leslie Stewart & Jeremy Paul

Moderately

mf 1. The child is a__ king, the ca - rol - lers__ sing, The

old is passed, there's a new be - gin - ning. Dreams of San - ta,

dreams of snow, Fin - gers numb, fa - ces a - glow. It's

Christ - mas time, mis - tle - toe and wine, Child - ren

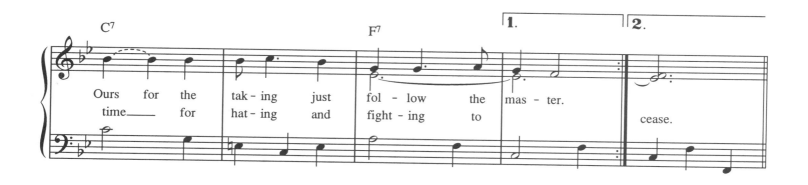

Ours for the | tak - ing just | fol - low the | mas - ter.
time___ for | hat - ing and | fight - ing to | cease.

Christ - mas time, | mis - tle-toe and | wine, | Child - ren sing - ing

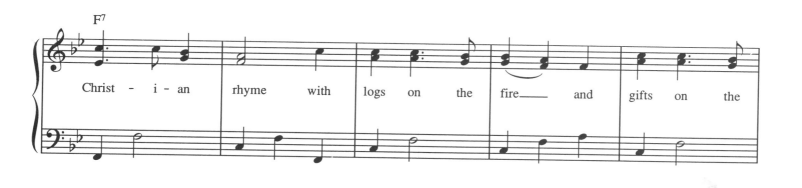

Christ - i - an rhyme with | logs on the | fire___ and | gifts on the

tree; A | time to re - | joice in the | good that we | see. | see.___

O Come All Ye Faithful

Traditional

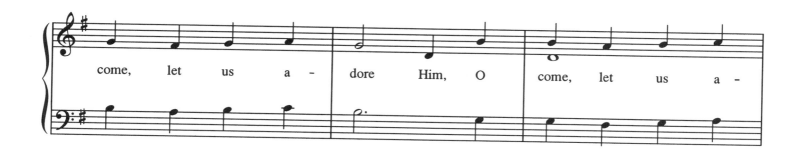

come, let us a - dore Him, O come, let us a -

dore Him, O come, let us a - dore Him,____

Christ_____ the Lord.   Lord.

Verse 2:

God of God,
Light of light,
Lo! He abhors not the Virgin's womb;
Very God, begotten not created;
    O come, let us *etc.*

Verse 3:

Sing, choirs of angels,
Sing in exultation;
Sing, all ye citizens of heav'n above;
'Glory to God in the highest:'
    O come, let us *etc.*

Verse 4:

Yea, Lord, we greet Thee,
Born this happy morning;
Jesu, to Thee be glory given;
Word of the Father, now in flesh appearing;
    O come, let us *etc.*

O Little Town Of Bethlehem

Traditional Christmas Carol

ev - er - last - ing light. The hopes and fears of

all ___ the ___ years are met in ___ thee to night. 2. O - el.

Verse 2:

O morning stars, together
Proclaim Thy holy birth.
And praises sing to God the King
And peace to men on earth.
For Christ is born of Mary,
And gather all above
While mortals sleep, the angels keep
Their watch of wond'ring love.

Verse 3:

How silently, how silently,
The wondrous gift is given!
So God imparts to human hearts
The blessings of His heaven.
No ear may hear His coming;
But in this world of sin,
Where meek souls will receive Him, still
The dear Christ enters in.

Verse 4:

O holy child of Bethlehem,
Descend to us we pray;
Cast out our sin and enter in,
Be born in us today.
We hear the Christmas Angels
The great glad tidings tell;
O come to us, abide with us,
Our Lord Emmanuel.

33

Once In Royal David's City

Traditional Christmas Carol

2. He came down to earth from heaven,
   Who is God and Lord of all;
   And His shelter was a stable,
   And His cradle was a stall.
   With the poor, and mean and lowly,
   Lived on earth our Saviour holy.

3. And our eyes at last shall see Him,
   Through His own redeeming love,
   For that Child so dear and gentle
   Is our Lord in heaven above;
   And He leads His children on
   To the place where He is gone.

Silent Night

Words & Music by Joseph Mohr & Franz Gruber

2. Silent night! Holy night!
Shepherds quail at the sight,
Glories stream from heav'n afar,
Heav'nly hosts sing Alleluia!
Christ the saviour is born,
Christ the saviour is born.

3. Silent night! Holy night!
Son of God, love's pure light;
Radiant beams Thy holy face
With the dawn of saving grace,
Jesus, Lord, at Thy birth,
Jesus, Lord, at Thy birth.

The First Nowell

Traditional

With movement

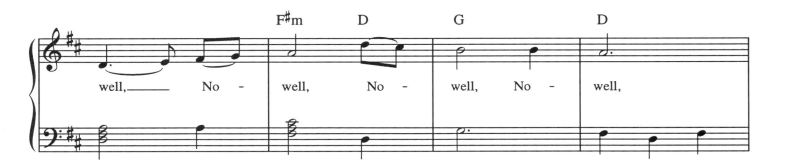

well,_____ No - well, No - well, No - well,

Born is the King___ of Is - ra - el. 2. They___ - el.

Verse 2:

They looked up and saw a star,
Shining in the East beyond them far,
And to the earth it gave great light,
And so it continued both day and night.
    Nowell *etc.*

Verse 3:

And by the light of that same star,
Three wise men came from country far;
To seek for a king was their intent,
And to follow the star wherever it went.
    Nowell *etc.*

Verse 4:

This star drew nigh to the north-west,
O'er Bethlehem it took its rest,
And there it did both stop and stay,
Right over the place where Jesus lay.
    Nowell *etc.*

Verse 5:

Then let us all with one accord,
Sing praises to our heavenly Lord,
That hath made heaven and earth of nought,
And with His blood mankind hath bought.
    Nowell *etc.*

When Santa Got Stuck Up The Chimney

Words & Music by Jimmy Grafton

While Shepherds Watched Their Flocks By Night

Traditional

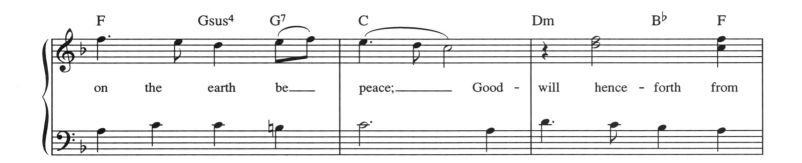

on the earth be____ peace;_____ Good - will hence - forth from

heaven____ to____ men be - gin and ne - ver____ cease."

Verse 2:

"Fear not," said he; for mighty dread
Had seized their troubled mind;
"Glad tidings of great joy I bring
To you and all mankind."

Verse 3:

"To you in David's town this day
Is born of David's line
A Saviour who is Christ the Lord;
And this shall be the sign."

Verse 4:

"The heavenly Babe you there shall find
To human view displayed,
All meanly wrapped in swathing bands
And in a manger laid."

Verse 5:

Thus spake the Seraph; and forthwith
Appeared a shining throng
Of Angels praising God, who thus
Addressed their joyful song.

Winter Wonderland

Words by Dick Smith ✠ Music by Felix Bernard

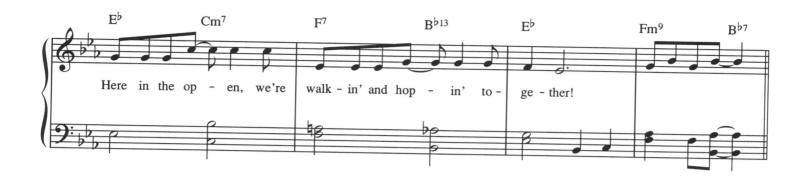

Here in the op - en, we're walk - in' and hop - in' to - ge - ther!

CHORUS

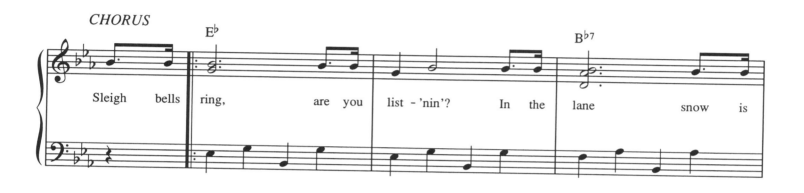

Sleigh bells ring, are you list - 'nin'? In the lane snow is

glist - 'nin', A beau - ti - ful sight, We're hap - py to - night,—

walk - in' in a win - ter won - der- land. Gone a - way is the

blue - bird, Here to stay is a new bird, he sings a love song,— As

we go a - long,— walk - in' in a win - ter won - der - land.

In the mea - dow we can build a snow - man, Then pre - tend that he is Par - son

Brown, He'll say "Are you mar - ried?" We'll say "No, man! But

you can do the job when you're in town!" La - ter on we'll con -

spire___ As we dream by the fire___ To

face un - a - fraid,___ the plans that we made,___ walk - in' in a win - ter won - der -

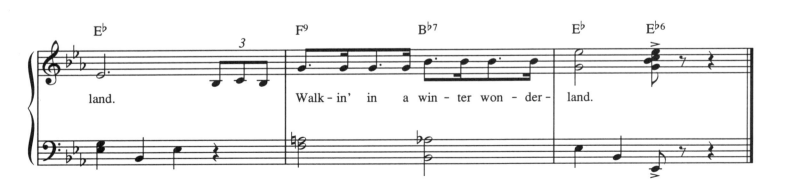

land. Walk - in' in a win - ter won - der - land.

Saviour's Day

Words & Music by Chris Eaton

Moderately

mf

1. Now we have been through the har-vest, win-ter has tru-ly be-gun; now we are walk-ing the chill of the night, we are wait-ing for, wait-ing for,— for the Sa-viour's Day.

2. Ma - ny have come from the val -leys,
(Verses 3 & 4 see block lyric)

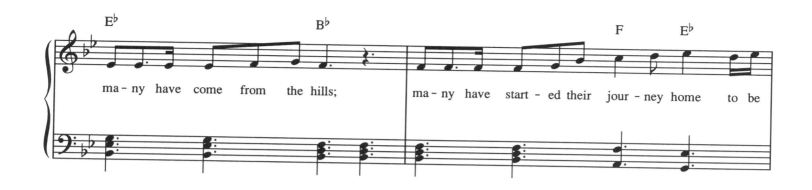

ma-ny have come from the hills; ma-ny have start-ed their jour-ney home to be

with some-one, with some-one___ on the Sa-viour's Day.___

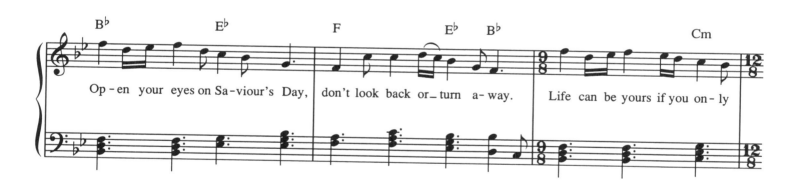

Op-en your eyes on Sa-viour's Day, don't look back or___ turn a-way. Life can be yours if you on-ly

stay,___ He is call-ing you, call-ing you___ on the Sa-viour's

Verse 3:

Joining the old and the young ones,
Joining the black and the white;
Meeting the need of the hungry is He,
Will we ever remember Him on the Saviour's Day.

Open your eyes on Saviour's Day,
Don't look back or turn away.
Life can be yours if you only stay,
He is calling you, calling you on the Saviour's Day.

Verse 4:

Here's to the God of the present, (raise your glasses)
Here's to the God of the past, (drink to the King)
Here's to the hope and the future He brings,
We will sing to Him, sing to Him on the Saviour's Day.

Open your eyes on Saviour's Day,
Don't look back or turn away.
Life can be yours if you only stay,
He is calling you, calling you on the Saviour's Day.